The

Cosmic Ordering
Wish Book
2010

The
Cosmic
Ordering
Wish Book
2010

Barbel Mohr and
Pierre Franckh

HAY HOUSE

Australia • Canada • Hong Kong • India
South Africa • United Kingdom • United States

First published and distributed in the United Kingdom by:
Hay House UK Ltd, 292B Kensal Rd, London W10 5BE. Tel.: (44) 20 8962 1230;
Fax: (44) 20 8962 1239. www.hayhouse.co.uk

Published and distributed in the United States of America by:
Hay House, Inc., PO Box 5100, Carlsbad, CA 92018-5100. Tel.: (1) 760 431 7695 or
(800) 654 5126; Fax: (1) 760 431 6948 or (800) 650 5115. www.hayhouse.com

Published and distributed in Australia by:
Hay House Australia Ltd, 18/36 Ralph St, Alexandria NSW 2015. Tel.: (61) 2 9669 4299;
Fax: (61) 2 9669 4144. www.hayhouse.com.au

Published and distributed in the Republic of South Africa by:
Hay House SA (Pty), Ltd, PO Box 990, Witkoppen 2068. Tel./Fax: (27) 11 467 8904.
www.hayhouse.co.za

Published and distributed in India by:
Hay House Publishers India, Muskaan Complex, Plot No.3, B-2, Vasant Kunj, New Delhi
– 110 070. Tel.: (91) 11 4176 1620; Fax: (91) 11 4176 1630. www.hayhouse.co.in

Distributed in Canada by:
Raincoast, 9050 Shaughnessy St, Vancouver, BC V6P 6E5. Tel.: (1) 604 323 7100;
Fax: (1) 604 323 2600

© Barbel Mohr and Pierre Franckh, 2009

The moral rights of the author have been asserted.

The author of this book does not dispense medical advice or prescribe the use of any
technique as a form of treatment for physical or medical problems without the advice of a
physician, either directly or indirectly. The intent of the author is only to offer information
of a general nature to help you in your quest for emotional and spiritual wellbeing. In the
event you use any of the information in this book for yourself, which is your constitutional
right, the author and the publisher assume no responsibility for your actions.

A catalogue record for this book is available from the British Library.

Previously published in German by Koha-Verlag GmbH, Burgrain, 2009,
ISBN 978-3-86728-090-7

Translation: Dennis McAllister, Nick Handforth www.citylanguages.de
Astrological and numerological consultant: Manfred Mohr

ISBN 978-1-84850-164-5

FSC
Mixed Source
Product group from well-
forests and other controll

Cert no. SGS-COC-2
www.fsc.org
© 1996 Forest Stewardship

Printed and bound in Great Britain by TJ International, Padstow, Cornwall.

Contents

Barbel Mohr and Cosmic Ordering

Barbel Mohr was a photo journalist, photo editor and graphic designer. In 1995 she then also started writing, at first just as a hobby. Her first book, *The Cosmic Ordering Service*, was a huge success. She has now sold over a million books and feedback from her readers proves how well her method works. She has also been giving lectures and seminars now for over 10 years. Her most successful seminar is the classic Life Happiness seminar which, among other things, strengthens the 'connection to above'.

'I discovered wishing and ordering for myself almost 15 years ago, though I hadn't believed in it at all before, and so opened the door to this wonderful world of new possibilities. The experiences of my circle of friends and readers have shown that what is most important when wishing or ordering, is what is so often important in life in general: 'Working together is better!' Whenever we came together and wished for something as a group, each wishing for themselves or all of us wishing for one thing, the success rate was often even higher.'

To read more by or about Barbel, visit
www.baerbelmohr.de

Pierre Franckh and Successful Wishing

☆☆☆☆

Author and actor Pierre Franckh specialises in the fields of psychology, relationships and eroticism. The result has been the bestselling books *Rules of Happiness for Love (Glücksregeln für die Liebe)*, *Loving Lustfully (Lustvoll Lieben)*, *Just Wish For It – But Do It Right! (Wünsch es dir einfach – aber richtig;* not available in English), *Just Wish For It – But Make It Easy (Wünsch es dir einfach – aber mit Leichtigkeit;* not available in English), and *Successful Wishing (Erfolgreich wünschen).*

He was a master of successful wishing even as a child, wishing himself a role in film and then acting opposite the star in the film about cheeky schoolboys by Ludwig Thoma. During his time at school, he lost this 'wonderful knowledge' which gave way to an enlightened, rational scepticism. He only found the path back to the skill of wishing through a crisis in his life. Wishing has now been a natural part of his life again for over 30 years. Pierre Franckh shares his knowledge and experiences in an inspiring way through his seminars and lectures. He shows us vividly in *Successful Wishing* that everything in life is made possible by using the power of wishing correctly. Enthusiastic feedback from his readers confirms how superbly his simple rules for wishing actually work in practice for everyone.

For more information, visit www.Pierre-Franckh.de

Wishes come true

Every day, every minute, every second.

We are constantly wishing for something,

Whether consciously or not.

We are even wishing when we don't want to wish.

What is your wish?

What do you want to bring into your life?

Instructions for Successful Wishing

From *Successful Wishing* by Pierre Franckh

1. Begin by wishing for little things ...

and allow your successes to convince your rational mind of the huge range of possibilities wishing offers. Nothing succeeds like success and one success naturally attracts further successes.

2. Always wish for things in the present tense

never in the future. *'I am rich'* and not *'I want to be rich.'* Otherwise you achieve the state of wanting something and not of being something.

3. Act as if you already have the thing you are wishing for

In this way you are constantly dealing with what is to come in a positive way and can prepare yourself by looking forward to it. This gives you the correct resonance and you literally draw the event into your life.
'Not' and 'nothing' do not exist in wishing. If you use these words, you draw all the things you want to avoid into your life because you give them energy through your thoughts. Anxious feelings attract the exact events you want to prevent from happening. 'I don't want to get ill,' in terms of wish energy means, 'I want to get ill.'

We can never prevent something from happening. We can only ever create something and never 'not create' something. Just the thought of 'not creating' it will make the unwanted thing happen, because we are thinking and worrying about it.

So wanting to avoid something doesn't work, but we can allow its opposite to take place. We just have to deal with its corresponding positive parallel.

'I am well.' This order is simple and clear. This wish allows us to focus on our health and not on illness.

4. Write the wish down

You give substance to your wish when you write it down. From then on it exists physically. It is your firm will, unshakeable, clear and unambiguous.

It also lets you check that the wish has been fulfilled. What did I really wish for and how must I improve my wording so that I receive the thing that I wish for from the bottom of my heart? Writing wishes down makes it easier to work with them. This diary is perfect for this purpose.

5. Clear, short and precise wording

The more precise you are in wording your wish, the more exactly it will be carried out. The more precise and succinct you are, the more you are forced to discover what lies at the heart of your wish. If you can express it in two sentences, you will be much more certain yourself about what you are really wishing for.

6. Giving thanks

You increase goodness by thanking, as you start to examine the things in your life which are going well. You give them attention and recognition. Whatever is given attention is also given energy. Giving thanks allows you to increase all of the good things that already exist in your life, because you give them even more energy.

Giving thanks brings the wish into the present. This is similar to saying 'Amen' at the end of a prayer. In translation, 'Amen' means 'Verily, it is so!' This means it is in the present. The energy from praying and wishing are very similar. In both cases we cry out to a higher power and ask for a solution. We sign off or close each by saying amen or by giving thanks.

Giving thanks sweeps away all doubt and worry. We believe it will happen. We are certain. In daily life you also only give thanks for things that you are sure will happen. 'Thank you for taking care of it for me.' So you only give thanks for things that you are absolutely certain will be carried out. By giving thanks, you are confirming your order. The wish is signed and sealed, like your signature at the end of a contract.

7. Trust instead of doubt

Doubt is a very clear wish that will be carried out. By doubting, you call your wishes back, almost before they have been sent out. Often, at the same time as making the wish, people say or think, 'It's not going to work anyway.' This thought, however, is nothing other than a precise wish, which is, 'Wishing doesn't work.' And what happens? This wish is sent out and will be delivered as ordered. We are always successful, most often by being the authors of our own failures. Those who don't believe in success cannot be successful. Therefore, always trust in the fact that your wish is going to be fulfilled.

8. Secrecy

You can weaken your wish by speaking about it. On the one hand, the energy is dissipated by the constant 'wear and tear' of discussing it. On the other hand, you quickly attract opposition from people who are jealous or doubt your plan, and you give space to their beliefs and convictions.

9. Forgetting

This has many advantages. Firstly, when you forget your wish, you then also forget to doubt and so prevent yourself from reversing the entire order process again. Secondly, you prove how great your trust is, as you are so certain that the thing you wish for will come into your life that you don't work at it any more. This also allows you to be open to accepting the thing you are wishing for when it arrives, no matter how awkward it might appear at the time.

10. Being open to coincidence

You can't plan the delivery of your wish. Wishes are almost always delivered in a way that you would never have believed possible, so you should simply just expect the wish to be fulfilled. The cosmos finds its own method of delivery and there is no way we can know what it will be.

11. Intuition

As everything is a question of energy, we are some-times 'only' guided very gently to the place where we can find the thing that we wish for. If you have sent out a wish, the best thing is to keep your ears pricked and to stay alert. This will let you gather all of the informa-tion you need. If you want to come into closer contact with your intuition, the only thing you have to do is to follow up on the things that feel right to you.

12. Discovering your great desires and heartfelt wishes

Which wishes suit me? This is the fundamental ques-tion. There is no point in wishing for something that goes against your own nature, though many of us do this anyway. We often wish for something just because others are wishing for it or already have it. We often pursue an ideal that isn't our own at all. Before we wish for something, we have to be clear that it is some-thing that we actually need in our lives. Will it make us feel better, more loveable, more accepted or happier? Every successful wish also changes our lives. This is why we should be absolutely sure that we are actually ready for this change. Find out what your true desires and heartfelt wishes are, so that they can also make you happy.

Wish, and be ready to let miracles into your life.

How Can I Use the Full Potential of This Diary?

The wonderful thing about this *Wish Book* is that it is the perfect way of learning how to wish.

1. First simply write down your wish in your diary

This will strengthen your wish. The wish physically leaves your body for the first time. It also gains strength just by doing so. Suddenly you are being serious about it. You are leaving the realms of speculation and dreams, which you still don't fully believe in. From now on your wish is physical; it is your stated will, unshakeable, clear and resolute.

If you just go about wishing willy-nilly, at some point you will no longer remember all of the things you have wished for and after a while, lose your overview. Added to this you don't usually wish for something by-the-by. You most probably wish for something then wish for the opposite, wish for the first thing again and then again for something completely different. We often don't really mean what we are wishing for, but were taken with the idea for a moment and a second later wish for something very different. The universe doesn't mind. Whatever is wished for will be delivered, even if we don't need it any more. We suddenly find ourselves buried in a heap of wishes we have sent out and no longer have an overview of our lives. Then all sorts of different and contradictory things start to happen all around us, and in the chaos we no longer realise that we are the authors of all of these events.

Added to this are all of our unconscious wishes that we really don't want to happen. Once again, we find ourselves back in the precise position we no longer wanted to be in: things happen and we don't have a clue who ordered all of them to happen. It is therefore better to be very deliberate in making our first wishes happen, to give them a clear direction and real weight by writing them down.

2. Then, over the following days, keep an eye out for any 'coincidences' which occur around you and note these down in your diary as well.

Just keep your eyes open and write everything down that attracts your attention. Some of these things will have nothing to do with your wish. Many, however, might do.

If you always keep looking in the only direction you expect the delivery to come from, it might be that you miss it completely, because you are waiting for the order to be fulfilled precisely as you expected – and our powers of imagination are very limited. The universe, however, is much more creative. Then when it does happens, we are happy to call it a miracle because we are so surprised that there have suddenly been so many 'coincidences' in our lives which led our wish to be fulfilled. In truth, it is all just part of the process of our wish becoming reality and this often happens in a way that we had not bargained for.

3. This diary helps to sharpen your intuition

Your intuition often leads you to stumble over the thing you wish for 'by coincidence'. This can sometimes be something that someone said, maybe something you happened to overhear which contained some vital piece of information. It can also be a sudden flash of inspiration you then follow up. Or you happen to choose to go somewhere by a different route and 'coincidentally' meet an old friend on the way who 'happens' to tell you about someone you ought to meet, and 'strangely enough' this person has the exact thing you wished for: a new apartment, the plunger to unblock your drains, or they know someone who can fix your computer problem.

If you want to get in contact with your intuition, you simply have to follow up on anything that feels right to you, no matter how strange, embarrassing or silly it might seem at first glance. Intuition is nothing more than making a spontaneous decision. If something occurs to you that you would like to do, then do it. Don't look for reasons for or against it. Don't weigh up the options, follow the impulse.

With the help of your intuition, your decisions will be more spontaneous and your trust in your own perceptions will grow. Instead of having to meet the challenges of daily life alone, you allow yourself to drift towards the solution you wished for. It is really nothing more than recapturing the etheric energy you sent out in the first place. In coming back to you, it now leads you to the place your wish will be fulfilled. You can see how wonderfully your intuition leads you by checking the entries you make in your diary.

4. Be aware of your own doubts

When wishes aren't fulfilled, it is usually because you have made a second wish which is stronger than the first. This second wish then works against the first, more forcefully and with greater determination. This second wish is mostly called 'doubt'.

Your conscious wish is often buried by unintentional doubts. You can see how effective wishing actually is by how persistently the negative or obstructing wish enters your life.

All of the positive thinking and all of the mantras in the world are no help if you are constantly thinking about problems and restrictions internally. Doubt is an attitude with deep roots, a firmly anchored belief that can make itself come true just as easily as your conscious wish. (For more on this, see the box on the following page.)

5. Checking your wishes

Have I got what I wished for? This is another advantage of writing things down in your diary; it forms a fabulous trail of evidence. After just a short time we often don't remember exactly what we have wished for any more. We still know the rough intention of our wish, but after a while the words can often get mixed up in our memory. This isn't surprising as countless new influences flood over us every single day. We change, our thoughts change and so do our memories, which often record an inseparable mixture of facts, thoughts and hopes.

If the wish is delivered and you can check the original

order again, you will often be wonderfully surprised. You will be amazed when you see how precisely the wish has been fulfilled according to your written order. Now you can start to work on our original wish wording. What have I received? Is it exactly what I wanted? If yes, hurray! If not: Which words do I have to change? Why was it fulfilled differently? Which words didn't fit the wish energy I sent out?

This helps you to word your wish better, more precisely, more exactly. What is it you actually want?

This guide will very quickly help you become a true wishing expert.

Working with the 'doubt cross'

Every time you have doubts about your wish, make a little cross next to it in the diary. You will be surprised how many little crosses pile up after a very short time.

This is just proof of how strongly you believe in the non-fulfilment of your wish. But having doubts isn't so bad if you don't take them too seriously. If you don't give your doubts any energy, they won't have any effect. The best thing is to accept the doubt, but not to spend time thinking about it. The doubts exist, they bubble to the surface, are noted – they are only doubts after all, which we shouldn't be giving any power or meaning – and are released again and sent on their way with no further thought.

Behind each 'doubt cross', add a 'take-no-notice-tick'. You will be surprised at how quickly over one year the doubts disappear as a deep-rooted basic trust enters your life.

Another method of Barbel's:

Just imagine that you are crossing out a doubt with each cross you make, and are taking away all its energy and force. All of the crosses in the diary are then all the doubts that you have 'located, holed and finally sunk' as if you were playing a game of Battleships. The more crosses you have, the more successful you were in 'doubt sinking'.

And now for some practical wishing tips from Barbel's *The Cosmic Ordering Service:*

The Cosmic Ordering Service

Unconscious thought patterns and doubts often put the brakes on wishes, so just try ordering from the cosmos. Our unconscious mind associates the word 'ordering' with a feeling of certainty that the order will arrive.

You can write your order down in your diary and imagine that you are sending 'a fax to the universe's mail-order warehouse'.

You then do exactly what you do with all other mail-order companies: get on with your daily tasks and stop thinking about it.

To strengthen your order you can practise your exercises in giving thanks. This leads to an automatic process of release at the level of the unconscious. In doing so, you divert your attention by concentrating on 'giving thanks for the little things' instead of 'worrying about when exactly your order is going to arrive'.

Act like the ancient Indians

Imagine what it would be like if you already had the thing that you wished for. How would you feel? What would your daily routine be like, how would it change? Experience the feeling as intensively as you can of, 'What it would be like, if only it were true?'. As soon as you can really feel it, give thanks for it. This is another powerful way of bringing your wish to life.

The Power of Togetherness

☆☆☆☆

The power of praying or wishing for others

Ho'oponopono is a Hawaiian healing technique that has many aspects. One of these states that you can heal everything inside yourself that you don't like around you. This is possible because all is one and the world, as we experience it, is only an illusion. Everything that exists is connected to, and influences, everything else. This doesn't only apply on the subatomic level, but also, according to Hawaiian philosophy, to the energetic and spiritual planes. 'Heal the resonances within yourself and others around you will cease to experience them'. This can even mean that people change their behaviour or become healthier because you stop feeling angry with them. Because you heal the resonances within yourself, you heal them in others as well. For more information, see *Cosmic Ordering: The Next Step*, by Barbel and Manfred Mohr, published by Hay House in September 2009.

Together for everyone

We can use this knowledge a) to send our own wishes into the cosmos on universal wish days, b) to make wishes for everyone else, the natural world and the entire planet.

My wish would be that as many of you as possible round off your very personal wishes and orders with the following words:

'...and I wish that the wishes of everybody else ordering and wishing along with me today are also fulfilled, to the good of those people and of everybody involved! I send out my thanks, my love and my wishes for healing to every level of planet Earth, the natural world and the entire universe'.

Even Einstein believed that the natural world tended towards harmony. When all people reconnect with their true, innermost nature and so achieve personal harmony and fulfilment, and wish exactly the same for everyone else, we will have achieved world peace! I am convinced of this.

Your Monthly Date with Yourself
☆☆☆☆

This diary offers you a wealth of information and topics for each month. All you need to do now is to take enough time to work with them …

The answer is simple: Make a date with yourself! Write down a time and date each month for you to meet yourself. Whether it's two, three or five hours or even a whole day depends on how it fits in with your life. You can manage two hours a month with a bit of organization, even if you have five children.

Maybe you want to start your date with yourself with a little meditation on self-love in front of the mirror. Then you can go through the topics for the month and make notes on where you are at the moment and where you want to be in your life. Examine your current situation honestly and love yourself in spite of, or because of, it.

Imagine the object of your wish as vividly as if it were already there. How would it feel? How would you feel with it? Write this feeling down in your diary and keep an eye on how it develops.

Round off your date with yourself by treating yourself to something good. I'm thinking less of shopping or TV and more of listening to your favourite music, having a long bath etc.

☆☆☆☆

Wish Dates
☆☆☆☆

The wish dates already marked in this diary are particularly favourable for sending off wishes and for ordering!

There are astrological and numerical dates, turbo-wish dates (which are universal wish dates where whole groups of people from the widest variety of countries and spiritual backgrounds all send their wishes off together), and there are also favourable wish dates chosen according to the Mayan calendar.

Astrologically chosen wish dates

Among the astrologically chosen dates are the new moon dates. You can wish all day long, but the force is strongest half an hour after the new moon has risen and for the following two hours. 'Those who count their money by the light of the new moon will never lack it,' and the Estonians speak to the new moon, saying, 'Greetings to you, moon, may you grow old and I stay young!', as Jacob Grimm wrote in his book, *German Mythology*.

The new moon strengthens all wishes which deal with new beginnings and with growth: more money, health, a new …

The full moon is a good time to let go of something, for example, to say goodbye to a bad habit. Then there are also times when aspects of certain topics are astrologically favourable. These are mostly several days in succession and you can see from the list of wish dates which symbols stand for which qualities.

Turbo-wish dates

The turbo-wish dates are specially selected and specify an exact time, which only lasts for a few minutes. This means that everyone making a wish on this date makes it at exactly the same time.

Whether it is because faith moves mountains, or if it is due to the synchronised timing or to the community of wishers, these dates have always worked especially well and have also led to wonderful meditation experiences and 'delivery success'
(see also www.21.17.com).

There are three turbo-wish dates with Barbel and Pierre once again this year.

You will find two extra little stars next to the turbo-wish symbol on three turbo-wish dates a year. This means that Barbel Mohr and Pierre Franckh will be wishing and ordering with you at exactly these times, for themselves and for everyone else.

Wish dates according to the Mayan Calendar

The Mayan calendar is an ancient calendar which has remained unchanged since Mayan times, unlike our Gregorian calendar, which was last altered in the 16th century. The start of the Mayan year is the 26th of July and not the 1st of January. The reason is that a particular constellation of stars can be seen in the sky on this day every year. On this day our sun is in conjunction with our second nearest star, Alcyone (in the Pleiadian system) and with the star Sirius B.

The final day of the Mayan year is the 24th of July and the remaining day, the 25th of July, is the so-called 'green day', the day outside time. This day connects the old year to the new.

Johann Koessner (www.maya.at), a famous Mayan calendar expert, writes that we also have a 'personal green day', which is the day before our birthday. It is a kind of personal day outside time and therefore also very favourable for wishing and for setting new impulses.

Your Daily Affirmation

☆☆☆☆

You will find a short sentence for each day in the diary. These affirmations have been created in such a way that they fit the special quality of that day. They will help you to work against unwanted things or strengthen the positive in a targeted way. They help us to centre our day and remind us of our true nature. If we consciously think of this sentence repeatedly throughout the day, it helps us to be true to ourselves and listen to our inner voice. This makes everything easier as it means we are in the flow of life.

Play with the affirmations, use them as the motto of the day and check in the evening how they have affected your day. You will notice after a very short time how much more consciously you live your life and this in itself has a positive effect on your wishing as it helps you to notice all the little signs, the 'coincidences', more easily through which your wish might just be fulfilled.

At the Beginning of Each Month

☆☆☆☆

At the beginning of each month you will find either the best wish formulations on a topic by Pierre or a success story from Barbel's readers.

Stories of successful ordering

These stories are meant to inspire you, so that you come up with lots of wonderful ideas and don't always just order yourself a parking space …

'Use it or lose it' as it is so neatly put – and this isn't just true for muscles but also for your connection to the universe!

'The only difference between a genius and an average person is that the genius has discovered their inner light and the average person has not!' (*The Genius Inherent in Everyone* by Walter Russell). In this way, these stories of success should also inspire you to communicate with your inner light more often.

Hot tip: don't just call the universe into your thoughts when you have a problem, but also share your happiness with it: 'Hey, universe, did you see that? – a great firework display, a laughing child, a great success – sooo beautiful, and I'm sending some of my joy up to you!' *This* exercises your connection to above as well!!!

If you have a particularly wonderful experience using one of the wish dates in this diary, you can email

them to kalender@baerbelmohr.de or kalender@
pierre-franckh.de and, if you are lucky, your story may
be published (for example in the next diary). With a
little bit more luck, you might win one of our three
surprise Christmas presents. For those who don't want
to be surprised, but would instead prefer to win a free
Life Happiness seminar with Barbel for two people,
or a one-to-one coaching session with Pierre, please
write to us and, of course, don't forget to include your
address!

Wish Meditations

My book *Successful Wishing* has been a surprise hit
over the past few years, and has positively changed the
life of a great many people. However, I am still asked in
my lectures and by email if there is a pre-worded guide
for all the various types of wishes. Although each wish
is truly individual, and in working with each person I
try to help them find the words to overcome their own
doubts, there is what you might call a 'template' that
works on a broad, general level. The following wish
meditations will lead you to a precisely defined energy
stream, so that everything inside you can open itself up
to whatever you would like to invite into your life.

The best thing to do each time you recite your wish
meditation is to create a concrete image of your very
personal wish immediately afterwards. Whatever it is,
let it play out like a little film in your mind's eye and
immerse yourself in it with the energy you have created
through your meditation. Whenever you notice that
doubts are beginning to rule your thoughts again, just
recite your wish sentence. It will bring you back into
the desired energy state again very quickly.

Key to Symbols

☆☆☆☆

All wish dates are astrological, numerical or selected by a

medium, or are a combination of all three.

 Job: You can wish for the perfect job, or a stress-free job and good communication on the days when you use this computer.

 Forgiveness: Forgiving yourself and others is a prerequisite for being able to love with your whole heart. Follow the dove and allow your love to grow.

 Changing old patterns: Wish for the necessary impulse to escape from the prison of unwanted but deep-rooted patterns and programmes.

 Spiritual encounters: Spirituality, erotic attraction and the pure love of life are all part of this.

 Feeling comfortable at home: A new home, peace with the neighbours, a new sofa and generally everything to do with living.

 Health: Order yourself help for health on all levels, to stay healthy or to become healthy, so that you can jump over all the obstacles in your path with the life-giving power of the sun.

Holidays: Today is the day for all wishes connected to your dream holiday.

Children: A harmonious family life is an important wish to make. Ideas and solutions for problems at school can also be ordered here.

The new moon: The new moon strengthens all wishes which deal with a new beginning or with growth (for more on this, see page 32) and the wish force is strongest half an hour after the new moon has risen and for the following two hours!

Full moon: The full moon is a good time to let go of something or to free yourself from bad habits. Above all, it is the ideal day for inner peace and reflection. Are my wishes truly heartfelt? Which signs and coincidences have already revealed themselves? In which situations have I listened to my inner voice and when haven't I?

Money: You can order money, or better yet, the thing that you want the money for. For example, order a house rather than the money to buy a house. This leaves more options open for the universe to deliver.

 Relationships: The days with the hearts are particularly suited for your wishes for harmony in your existing relationship or for a new partner if you are single.

 Turbo-wish dates: The turbo dates selected by the mediums are particularly powerful as they only last for a few minutes and as everyone who is taking part is wishing at exactly the same moment, which amplifies the power.

 Turbo-wish date plus: Barbel and Pierre will be wishing and ordering at this exact time on three dates in the year, for themselves and for the fulfilment of the wishes of everyone taking part at that very moment.

The effect of the moon on star signs

The moon spends about two to three days each month in each star sign on its journey through the zodiac. Since the moon represents feelings, in astrological terms, it affects our emotions most strongly and these are vital to our creativity (for example, if we feel worthless, we won't be able to create anything worthwhile). So the moon shows us which days are particularly suitable for us to feel our way into certain topics and so be able to influence them positively. However, the resonance of the moon is not very dominant and the wish symbols have a stronger influence. Moon phases are therefore particularly interesting for wishing on the days when no more dominant prevailing influence exists.

The moon in Gemini: Mercurial, agile and versatile, enthusiastic and mentally alert. A good day for all things related to children, and for new ideas.

The moon in Cancer: Intense and deep feelings, domestic, providing and seeking a feeling of security, the ability to empathize. A good day for togetherness and for spending at home.

The moon in Leo: Decisive, energetic, enjoyment of risk, a lust for life, hungry for adventure. A good day for sensual encounters, children and entertainment.

The moon in Virgo: Exact, logical, methodical, taking small, well-considered steps. A good day for work, money and health.

The moon in Libra: Balance, providing and seeking harmony, artistic and aesthetic. A good day for family and friends.

The moon in Scorpio: The urge to discover, erotic attraction, concentration on concepts or opportunities for transformation. A good day for sensual encounters and for dissolving old patterns of behavior.

The moon in Sagittarius: Strong visionary powers, idealizing, creative. A good day for spirituality and voyages of discovery, both inside and out.

The moon in Capricorn: Objective, straight, success orientated, serious and prepared to work, clear thought. A good day for work and money.

The moon in Aquarius: Mercurial and intuitive, freedom loving, breaking chains, helping others. A good day for encounters, friends and quantum leaps.

The moon in Pisces: Absorbing the feelings of others like a sponge, empathetic, full of fantasy, altruistic. A good day for forgiveness and spending a day alone with yourself.

The moon in Aries: Impatient, agitated, wanting 'to bang your head against a brick wall' but also impulsive. A good day to tackle something new.

The moon in Taurus: Persevering, slow, dogged, realistic and safety-conscious. A good day for financial and domestic affairs.

A motto for each day of the week to strengthen your personality and intuition and improve your wish fulfilment

Monday: this is the day for a new beginning. Whatever you want to change or to do differently, Monday is always a good time to start. Monday is also a good day for thinking about things in a new way.

Tuesday: this day is totally dedicated to serving the universe. Today I will pay close attention to impulses and to 'signs from above'.

Wednesday: I will be completely calm and centred today, no matter what happens.

Thursday: Today I will stand up for myself and even use a 'cleansing thunderstorm', if necessary.

Friday: Today I am free of all negative thoughts. On this day I will pay attention only to positive things.

Saturday: The name Saturday comes from the old German word *Sambaztac*, in Hebrew, *Schabbat*, and in Latin *Sabbata*. This is a holiday in the Christian community of Seventh Day Adventists (also see Schabbat). We accept this meaning and use Saturday to relax and to enter stillness and peace, even if this is only for half an hour. Stillness gives your soul the space to reveal your calling and your heartfelt wishes to you more clearly.

Sunday: The day of the Sun and of Yang energy. Exercise outside in the fresh air is good on this day.

Treat This as a Little Exercise Book
☆☆☆☆

This is why your daily entries are so important. You can trace your wishes from their creation, through their development, through the apparent 'coincidences' connected to them, your changing attitudes to your wishes and, of course, the number of doubt crosses. This is how we come to understand what we really believe about ourselves. Only once we discover what we really want can we begin to give direction to working with our wishes.

And naturally we will increasingly have more than one wish at the same time. Therefore it is good to work with abbreviations or initials for each wish (see below for some ideas). We have big wishes and little wishes. Some are delivered straight away, others take longer to process and, of course, sometimes only our doubts are delivered.

Keep this little book for a few years so that you can check how successful you have been and how expertly you now go about your daily wishing in practice.

Examples of wishes:
PS: Parking space
W1: Wish one: relationship
W2: Wish two: a new vacuum cleaner
W3: Wish three: tickets for a festival
W4: Wish four: I am beautiful
W5: Wish five: I am amazingly beautiful
W6: Wish six: new clothes for my date
X: doubt cross

Successful Wishing

☆☆☆☆

The Healing Power of Music

The knowledge of resonance and its effect is ancient. The ancient Egyptians, Plato and Pythagoras knew about the effects of sound, so it is not surprising that even the scientists of today are very active in trying to discover the effects of sounds and vibrations. We now know that each individual cell has its own frequency and its very own resonance, and that this can be changed by the quality of sounds. If we listen to wonderful, uplifting music, each individual cell in our body will blossom with shining beauty and we very soon find ourselves filled with a wonderful wish energy. The more harmonious and pure the music we are listening to, the more we find ourselves in tune with beauty and grace.

Even a simple tuning fork can be used effectively to help us relax. It has been shown that tuning forks get our cranio-sacral fluid flowing again, which is the fluid that is in direct contact with our nervous system. The wonderful thing about a simple tuning fork is that it works through the subconscious. We don't have to think about it, we don't have to understand or consider anything. The sound alone reorganizes our entire field of resonance.

We come back into harmony with ourselves. Our thoughts and feelings change and the whole of our body assumes a completely new posture. Without having to use our rational mind, we are quickly back in tune with ourselves. All disharmonies in our body dissipate and we are brought back into resonance with a universal frequency.

Then we might suddenly have completely new ideas, or solutions for problems can appear that we would not have thought of before.

When we are fully relaxed, old patterns of behaviour and wounds can be examined and released. There is nothing more profoundly effective than when we are connected to a healing resonance. You might feel like getting a tuning fork and trying this out. Go ahead and try it out – especially when you feel tired or washed-out, angry or out of balance. Just tap the tuning fork, listen to the sound and wait to see what happens. So it is sometimes very simple to raise the level of our field of resonance and so to enter the best possible state of wish energy.

☆ ☆ ☆

Weekly Diary
2010

28 monday

My ideals are becoming clear to me

29 tuesday

I am glad to be independent

30 wednesday

I am showing my best side to the world

31 thursday
New Years Eve   20:00

I dedicate this day to reviewing the year gone by

friday **1**
New Years Day

This year is a good year for me

saturday **2**

I only expect the best from today

sunday **3**

I spread my creative wings today

wish notes for the week

January 2010 week 1

4 monday

I accept the darker sides of me

5 tuesday

I have the strength to deal with daily life

6 wednesday

I am aware of my own value

7 thursday

I find myself through peace

friday **8**

I am the way that I am

saturday **9**

I take responsibility for myself

sunday **10**

I am childlike and lively

wish notes for the week

January 2010 week 2

11 monday

I have the power to overcome challenges

12 tuesday

I am sensitive to the feelings of others

13 wednesday

I am beautiful

14 thursday

I trust in my inner guide

○ friday **15**
07:11

I trust in my strength

saturday **16**

I allow myself to express my creativity freely

sunday **17**

17:10–17:20

I discover the power of freedom

wish notes for the week

January 2010 week 3

18 monday

I feel at home within myself

19 tuesday

I follow my inspiration

20 wednesday

My intuition shows me the way

21 thursday

I discover my own beauty

friday **22**

I organize my life

 saturday **23**

I concentrate on what is essential

 sunday **24**

I break free from old chains

wish notes for the week

January 2010 week 4

25 monday

I follow my own senses

26 tuesday

I judge my situation correctly

27 wednesday

Every coincidence has a deeper meaning

28 thursday

I can withstand pressure

friday **29**

My family gives me strength

saturday **30**

06:18

I give space to the child inside me

sunday **31**

I let my creativity run wild

wish notes for the week

Successful Orders

☆☆☆☆

The universe sees the bigger picture

A participant in one of my Life Happiness seminars told me that the parking space orders really did always work well. With one exception. Once he had to look for a very long time for a space and in the end had to park quite a long way away. When he finally arrived at the venue where he was supposed to be giving a course, it turned out that not a single student was there because the course had been cancelled for that day. He found this amazing. It was as if the universe already knew that he didn't actually need a parking space on that day.

Even modern science (e.g. in the Russian Academy of Sciences) has discovered signs that a part of us always knows where everything else in the universe is and what is being created or carried out at any given moment. Each proton (a subatomic particle) in the world knows at any point in time where it is in the universe, to within a meter. And it can exchange information at any time with all of the other subatomic particles in the world.

What is your body made of? Atoms, of course. This means that each little atom within us knows where we are, where everything else is and what we need in order to fulfil our maximum potential.

So when we feel lost, uncertain and helpless, then the surest path to our ideal position in life leads through our inner self. If you love yourself as you are; if you forgive yourself everything that you are unhappy about; if you truly accept yourself and your feelings, then you are in ideal contact with yourself and your inner guide. Whether this guide is subatomic or purely spiritual shouldn't matter to us at all. It is there and it is real. If the thing you ordered does not appear in your life immediately:

• Strengthen your love for yourself. Look into a mirror as often as possible and say to yourself: 'I love me.'

• Keep a self-love diary and every evening write what you have done well that day in it, no matter whether it is something big or something absolutely tiny. Start each day by reading at least one entry to remind you that you have done something really well.

• Ask the universe to help show you how you might be blocking your flow of energy. Lean back more often, breathe and relax. Try counting to three when you breathe in through your nose, hold your breath for three seconds, breathe out for three seconds through your mouth, hold your breath again for three seconds and then start again from the beginning. Two or three of these breathing cycles are enough to give you a little break from day-to-day worries. Afterwards, feel into your heart and ask it what you can do to connect yourself more deeply and strongly with the source of the universe.

February 2010 week 5

1 monday

I am aware of the emotions attached to me

2 tuesday

Every new thing enriches me

3 wednesday

The clearer I am, the truer my relationship is

4 thursday

I am full of happy expectation for this year

friday **5**

I look behind the surface of things

                                          saturday **6**

If I trust in the power of my soul, I am healed

                                           sunday **7**

I can be completely childlike today

wish notes for the week

February 2010 week 6

8 monday

I accept that things can also be easy sometimes

9 tuesday

I let my heart speak out today

10 wednesday

I am in harmony with nature

11 thursday

I am open to new ideas

week 6 **2010 February**

friday **12**

I am full of thanks and happiness

saturday **13**

I stand firm

sunday **14**

02:51 Chinese New Year
Valentine's Day

This day, light as a feather, I give myself as a gift

wish notes for the week

February 2010 week 7

15 monday

I let my feelings speak out

16 tuesday
Pancake Day

Deep feelings and lightness go hand in hand

17 wednesday

17:10–17.20

I am the master of my emotions

18 thursday

My emotions lead me to my own truth

friday **19**

I shape my life according to my wishes

 saturday **20**

I combine work and pleasure in my life

 sunday **21**

I give a clear structure to my wishes

wish notes for the week

February 2010 week 8

22 monday

I can express myself well

23 tuesday

I plan my future with complete confidence

24 wednesday

I forgive myself and others

25 ~~thursday~~

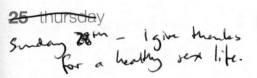
Sunday 28th - I give thanks for a healthy sex life.

My feelings are reflected in my actions in complete harmo

friday **26**

I feel safe and secure at home

Barry wish - love life back.

Lucie wish :-

saturday **27**

Hear my inner higher self for guidance

I am open to new feelings

Slingest $\frac{1}{2}$ hr after new

sunday **28**

16:38

moon has risen and then for the following 2 nows

(New Moon)

Peace is the path to power

→ new beginnings with growth money health jobs

→ let go of a bad habit → (Full Moon)

↑ p 31

wish notes for the week

Sunday wish
Please help me find a good and fulfilling job that serves and brings abundance.
Please help find a lovely home in Wales near my family and a satisfying job where
Please help Birgitta in recognition on Tuesday so she is feeling not going

Successful Wishing

☆☆☆☆

The fear of losing money

The thing that people who have finally come into money worry most about is that they might lose it all again. Having this very fear, though, is the beginning of the end. The loss they could suffer is foremost in their minds and not the wonderful feeling of having. The correct thing to do is to paint a positive picture of retaining the money to allow this image to become reality. There is not much point in worrying about the stock market or the value of our shares. Instead we should think as often as possible about how cleverly and well our money has been invested.

All of my finances are in very capable hands and are making a constant profit for me.

If we repeat this sentence occasionally to ourselves, above all when we notice that our doubts are gaining the upper hand again, and when we believe in the efficacy and power of the statement with all our heart, then we will draw this precise energy into our lives. Then we will find the right advisors at our side who will choose the best investments at the right time, who will make no losses but on the contrary continually increase our fortune. It doesn't matter at all how the economy is doing, nor does it matter if others try to scare us with their fears of loss by painting pictures of catastrophes for us. The only important thing is how we see it.

How Gerit's life changed overnight

I bought your book the day before yesterday and 'devoured' it in just a couple of hours. Then yesterday I began to think and wish according to your recommendations and rules. And whether you believe it or not – today I am already free of a great deal of my worries. The universe delivers, and it delivers quickly. Frighteningly fast, if you do it right.

I am the owner of a fireworks company and just a couple of days ago didn't even know how I was going to keep the company going. At night I dreamt of bankruptcy and bailiffs. And today, just two days after reading your book and thinking in the way you recommend, two important business partners have made a concrete offer to help me through the next few months, and maybe the coming years. So this isn't just a temporary respite, but a permanent one! Yesterday I simply did precisely what you recommend in your book, and today my life changed completely. It is incredible. Thank you!

March 2010 week 9

1 monday

Barry wish :- Thank you for my affulence.

2 tuesday

Luce wish - Thank you for helping Brigitta in court tomorrow. Giving her strength and clear speech so he count see her as non guilty.

I allow myself my freedom

I gather new strength through peace

3 wednesday

I give thanks for a safe journey to India today For myself and Barry.

I say yes to a harmonious relationship

4 thursday

I find my truth deep within me

Wishing for a safe **friday 5**
and happy holiday and
everything is fine at home.
I allow myself to be big → First treatment
day in India.

saturday 6

Everything comes around in its own time

sunday 7

Words can heal

wish notes for the week

March 2010 week 10

8 monday

I wish to be

Free from the prison of unwanted but deep rooted patterns and programmes. The recurring patterns manifest themselves to me so I discover what they are.

I discover a recurring theme in my life

9 tuesday

I wish to have a marvellous holiday in Kerala, may it continue to be a calm, ~~and~~ cleansing and enlightening experience when we leave Joga Village and go to our ~~next~~ destination.

I find myself in nature

10 wednesday

I let go of old ~~patterns~~ that no longer fit in with my life, if they ever did. I do this with clear thought and perception. ~~Self~~ discovery

I let go of something that does not fit in my life

11 thursday

I set myself goals

I wish to make quantum leaps   **friday 12**
and progress in expansiveness.
make encounters and discoveries
and change old patterns

I motivate myself today

I wish to receive   **saturday 13**
rupees so
we can pay our bill at Poopalleys
catch a taxi to Cochin, enjoy Cochin
and catch a taxi to the airport.

Everything is light and flowing

Please bring us rupees very soon.

Please send us   **sunday 14**
enough rupees tomorrow   Mother's Day
so we can afford Cochin and
enjoy ourselves and get to

I have consideration for the feelings of others

the airport.

wish notes for the week

Therapy
session with Dianne
- Need to realize my power, and
start to express myself and
be more expansive.
- I hope to get constitution
analysis with the doctor
before I leave the yoga
village.

March 2010 week 11

15 monday ◯   I wish that

21:01   I am able to

withdraw enough ruppes tomorow

so we can afford getting to Cochin

A good day for wishing. A good day to implement big plans

and enjoying ourselves and then getth

the flight back home. Thankyou

16 tuesday   I wish to

start new beginnings when I

get home, I wish to be more

expansive and expressive and

start acting on my   *I grow into my challenges*

own power and will make

changes to make my life better.

17 wednesday ☆ 🦂

I give thanks for a safe

journey for myself and   17:10–17:20

Barry back to England.

I start tackling things

18 thursday 🦂

I wish to create

a new way forward

in my career, find

a role that makes   *I strive for harmony*

me happy and fits

in with my life.

friday **19**

I engage actively with others

saturday **20**

Spring Equinox

I wish for the perfect job situation, helping my life and keeping me busy motivated and satisfied. I will pursue

I pursue my goals with determination

my goals with determination

sunday **21**

I wish to find some direction in my career and start to form plans for the future. Please help me discover

I discover my inner beauty

my Divine guidance

---

wish notes for the week

Start to make steps towards my new life where I am happier, doing what I should be doing and more powerful.

Please help with the rupees.

March 2010 week 12

22 monday

My own clarity lets me grow

23 tuesday Give my sight
clarity for the road
ahead.
Give me strength *I go my own way*
to follow my own way

24 wednesday

If this day were my last, what would I still like to do?

25 thursday

I love myself

friday **26**

Tension also brings positive changes

saturday **27**

I have the strength to offer others protection

sunday **28**
Palm Sunday
Beginning of British Summer Time

I yearn for deeper understanding

wish notes for the week

Lets go Forward
with my new plans
follow my divine guidance

Successful Orders

The universe has a sense of humour

A friend of mine, who is also the mother of my children's best friend, told me a funny story about one of her friends. She had got lost somewhere in her car, tried and tried but couldn't find the street she was looking for. In her despair, she finally even turned to some soft toys which she always kept in her car: 'Dear toys, please help me. I have no idea what to do…' At the next lights she had had enough. She quickly jumped out of her car and knocked on the window of the car next to her to ask the driver the way to the street in question. The woman promptly answered:

'Oh, that's exactly where I am going too. Why don't you just follow me?'

'And shall I tell you something?' said the lost lady to my friend later: 'The other car was full of soft toys! Isn't that crazy? It's as if the toys started a soft toy call-out to find out how we could get to our destination.'

You have probably noticed this yourself: The universe almost always delivers in a different way to what we expect. So thinking about how this or that could possibly happen is often pointless. If you always do your best in any situation in life, you will have the best possible connection and the universe can deliver and create new opportunities for you in its own creative way.

We reap what we sow, but the difference with farming is that the fruits very often grow in a completely different place to the one where we planted the seed.

For example, I support a poor family by babysitting and on the way home the local farmer gives me a box of vegetables. I take time for lonely people, although I am actually very busy and suddenly a friend calls me up out of the blue and takes another of my responsibilities off my hands, completely unexpectedly. I donate money to an institution and it returns to me from a very different source. Why does this happen? Because life loves to express its humour and to wrap it up in lots of small and large surprises. The universe usually doesn't deliver in a linear way. You can never tell how in advance.

March/April 2010 week 13

29 monday

I don't have to do everything by myself

30 tuesday ⚪
02:25

I realize how important my family is to me

31 wednesday ♎

I trust my intuition

1 thursday

Can I please be healthy

I rejoice in life

friday **2**
Good Friday

I find my truth deep within me

saturday **3**

My intuition tells me what to do

sunday **4**
Easter Sunday

I am here for me

wish notes for the week

April 2010 week 14

5 monday
Easter Monday

I am in harmony with my intuition

6 tuesday

My male and female sides are in unison

7 wednesday

I see the beauty in every moment

8 thursday

I discover my true dreams

friday **9**

I help my feelings express themselves

 saturday **10**

All is good and complete

 sunday **11**

I give free reign to my creativity

wish notes for the week

April 2010 week 15

12 monday

Please bring me
Clarity + motivation in
my career.

I bring my creativity to the fore

---

13 tuesday

My inner equilibrium radiates out of me

---

14 wednesday ○
12:29

A good wish day. A wonderful day to experience my
own beauty

---

15 thursday

I live out my own inner strength

friday **16**

I am true to myself

   saturday **17**

17:10–17:20

I trust in the rhythms of life

  sunday **18**

I see everything in a new light

wish notes for the week

April 2010 week 16

19 monday

I make my visions real

20 tuesday

I dedicate myself to my tasks

21 wednesday

I accept my female side with open arms

22 thursday

Spiritual understanding strengthens me

friday **23**

I am ready for new things

  saturday **24**

I face up to my fears

 sunday **25**

I act according to my inner feelings

wish notes for the week

Successful Wishing

☆☆☆☆

The wish collage

The longer and more intensively we work with our wish, the more intensive and sustained the energy is that we project into our surroundings. This might sound like a lot of work, but in reality isn't any effort at all. You can easily come into resonance with your wishes in a playful way. To be precise, it is actually best if we are completely relaxed when wishing. The easier it is for us, the better.

And now I'm happy to be able to tell you how you can achieve this lightness as I have been doing this myself for years with great success:

• Cut out everything that you would like to have in your life from magazines or catalogues – whatever it may be. Any pictures, drawings or photos which have a connection to your wish are suitable. And don't limit yourself in the number or type of things that you would really like to have in your life. Maybe it is a computer, a bicycle, a house, a dress or a car. Maybe it is several things at once. An apartment, rollerblades, a bag, a boat, a holiday, your dream partner or money.

• Whatever you would like to have in your life should be included in this picture. You are making a collage. You can also draw or write something on your picture, the format is up to you. The most important thing is that you have this picture – or rather your wishes – to look at again and again, and that you engage with it. Every time you see your heart's desire before you, your subconscious basks in expectant happiness. You begin to accept the object of your dreams more and more. You identify with your wishes. You get ever closer to your goals. They are no longer out of reach, and all of a sudden they are fulfilled. And you find this natural. Because they have been a part of you for such a long time, it is only natural for you to be able to welcome them into your life physically, in very concrete terms.

• Hang this picture up at home, so that you come into contact with it every day.

• Maybe you sometimes add something new to it, or you fill in more of the details.

• The more your spirit and your imagination focus on the object of your wish, the more you engage with it, the sooner it will be drawn into your life.

• The more you are in a state of happy expectation, the stronger the energy you send out.

• Bond with your picture. This is your wonderful future.

26 monday

I am aware of my masks

27 tuesday

I use my energy to wish successfully

28 wednesday
12:18

Everything is happening as it should

29 thursday

I am interested and open for everything I encounter

friday **30**

I follow my intuition

saturday **1**

I can look after myself

sunday **2**

① → Crown
② → Forehead
③ → Heart
④ → Sacral
⑤ → Throat
⑥ → Navel

The only boundaries are those in my mind

⑦ → Base

wish notes for the week

May 2010 week 18

3 monday
May Bank Holiday

I am open and ready for change

4 tuesday

I am curious to find happiness

5 wednesday

I can also enjoy new things

6 thursday

I entice myself to follow new paths

friday **7**

Friends enrich my life

saturday **8**

There is a ready solution for every problem

sunday **9**

*I have the strength and the self-confidence to deal
with criticism*

wish notes for the week

May 2010 week 19

10 monday

I am enthusiastic about my life

11 tuesday

I am open to creative stimulation

12 wednesday

New friends give me new inspiration

13 thursday

I stand up for my ideals

◯ friday **14**
01:04

Abundance can also be found in small details

  saturday **15**

I discover the power of words

  sunday **16**

I can discover adventures, even in my daily life

wish notes for the week

May 2010 week 20

17 monday

Thank you for
bringing Birgitta
home safely

17:10–17:20

I am open for new things

18 tuesday

Please give
me good
communication skills
and the perfect job.
Thanks.

I enjoy my energy and drive

19 wednesday

I am inspired by
new ideas today
I am energetic +
vital.

I let myself be inspired by new ideas

20 thursday

Thank you for my
Dad's safe journey

New things appear as if by themselves

Save to his ship

I love this day. it works for me
I am logical and in harmony
with my friends.
thank you friday **21**

For my Dad's
safe journey back to
his ship. Please protect him

This day is unfolding just for me

Thank you for my
dad's safe
journey back to his
ship.

saturday **22**

I listen to my gut feeling

sunday **23**
Whitsun

I enchant those around me

wish notes for the week

24 monday

*I am part of the whole and engage with others
powerfully*

25 tuesday

I express my feelings often and honestly

26 wednesday

I am permanently looking for new things

27 thursday
23:07

I am following a new dream

Thank you for showing me the way

friday **28**

I let myself be inspired by feelings

saturday **29**

I can let go of old things

sunday **30**
Spring Bank Holiday

I enjoy being inventive

wish notes for the week

Please offer me new avenues to discover.

Successful Ordering

Warm sleeping bag delivered

Lars loves riding his bike. One time he cycled from San Francisco to San Diego and wanted to travel inland from there, through the desert. He was a little bit worried, though, because he only had a thin summer sleeping bag and knew that it could get very cold at night in the desert. He didn't have enough money to buy a warmer one, so he trusted that everything would work out well and went into a café to have something to drink before he set off into the desert. A short time later a woman came into the café, and although there were hardly any other guests there, asked Lars if the table next to him was free.

It came out that she wanted to talk to him because she yearned to travel through the country as freely as he. In the course of the conversation she discovered where he was going and noticed his thin summer sleeping bag. She suddenly offered to give him her old winter sleeping bag. So she took him to her apartment and gave him a wonderful and luxuriously warm winter sleeping bag which got him through the desert perfectly.

We often think, 'If only I were rich, then everything would be just fine…' Maybe this is the real reason why so many millionaires are terribly bored and feel anything but fulfilled and happy. Only those people are happy who possess at least as much inner as outer abundance. It is never the universe that does not want to deliver. It is always the person who does not see the opportunity. Local currencies are an example of just such an opportunity to be able to afford a lot of things, even without money. Have a look at www.margritkennedy.de – or Google the search terms 'local currencies', 'barter currencies' and 'gift economy'.

Laila Schmid, who co-authored the book *Arbeitslos und trotzdem glücklich: Chancen ergreifen und die Zeit sinnvoll nutzen (Unemployed but Still Happy)* with me, said that since she became unemployed, she has been to more seminars than ever in her life before. She had neither earned enough money while she was working to be able to afford as many nor had she enough holiday to be able to go to them. Our true nature as people lies in giving freely, both sharing and accepting gifts just as readily. People and opportunities such as these are already there – you just have to open your eyes and look around you!

May/June 2010 week 22

31 monday

I am open for deep emotional discussions

1 tuesday

I am happy and relaxed

2 wednesday

I give myself a gift

3 thursday

I enjoy what I have

week 22 2010 June

 friday **4**

Dreams can also come true

 saturday **5**

I thank my parents for everything

 sunday **6**

I reveal myself

wish notes for the week

June 2010 week 23

7 monday

I can find creative beauty even in daily life

8 tuesday

I do something that I have never done before

9 wednesday

I enjoy being aware

10 thursday

My body is a gift from God

friday **11**

I live spontaneously, flexibly, and my spirit is free

  saturday **12**

11:15

I am really going to enjoy myself today

  sunday **13**

Power and strength are with me today

wish notes for the week

June 2010 week 24

14 monday

I am lively and full of power

15 tuesday

I enjoy the lightness in my life

16 wednesday

I am glad to be here on Earth

17 thursday
17:10–17:20

I love all aspects of my personality

friday **18**

Every challenge makes me stronger

saturday **19**

I am allowed to enjoy life

sunday **20**
Father's Day

Clear structures help me to master my life

wish notes for the week

June 2010 week 25

21 monday
Summer Solstice

I am open and ready for a deep and loving relationship

22 tuesday

I am proud of my achievements

23 wednesday

I plan my life myself

24 thursday

I always only find the truth within myself

friday **25**

I pay attention to my body and take enough exercise

   ◯ saturday **26**
11:30

I have both feet firmly on the ground

sunday **27**

I am worth dedicating an entire day to myself

wish notes for the week

Successful Wishing

☆☆☆☆

Ten key rules for drawing wealth into your life

1. Don't make any long excuses to explain how you are doing at the moment – neither to yourself nor to others. Instead, describe to your subconscious how wonderful everything is at present.

2. Be adamant in your belief that you deserve to have money – regardless of how badly the economy is doing and how many stock market crashes you read about. Firmly believe that you can afford everything that you want and that you can live in the way that you feel you deserve.

3. Always keep a secure hold on your vision. Wealth is your natural state, money is available in abundance. By holding on to this thought tightly, we bring ourselves in resonance with the energy of wealth.

4. Feel rich. Like attracts like.

5. Think yourself rich. An external lack of something can always be traced back to an internal lack. We usually don't think ourselves rich, but rather feel neglected, emotionally impoverished and unloved. This very often leads to the thought that we don't deserve anything. In this case our aphorism should be, 'Life is wonderful and provides me with everything I need.'

6. There is no emotion to money. It is only a means of exchange.

7. If we want to draw money into our lives it is vital to our success to be sure that we would actually also welcome money into our lives.

8. Let the money flow. Don't try to hoard money – this only sends out the energy that you are expecting an emergency. If you repeatedly suffer financial shocks, times of emergency, the one and only reason for this is that it stems from the expectation you have of life.

9. Of course we can set aside money for specific things, for retirement, for a bicycle, a new computer, for a holiday, a house or a car… We connect ourselves with happiness through these things. We feel wealthy and are happy to bring this money back into circulation at the right point in time. The most important thing to remember here is that the money must continue to flow so that it remains alive and energetic.

10. When we have money, we should also think of others who aren't doing as well, and let them share in our wealth. This not only brings joy to us, but also allows a feeling of wealth to be created. We are only rich enough in our minds when we can give some of our wealth lightly to others. If instead, we are miserly and squirrel the money away, we mistrust the natural flow of money and unintentionally cut ourselves off from life. This means that we don't really believe that money will flow back to us.

June/July 2010 week 26

28 monday

I support myself with love

29 tuesday

Happiness is my natural state of being

30 wednesday

Every dream contains an unfulfilled desire

1 thursday

I feel like a king

friday **2**

I dedicate this day to my friends

saturday **3**

I can be proud of myself

sunday **4**

I sample the cornucopia of life

wish notes for the week

July 2010 week 27

5 monday

I am proud of my achievements

6 tuesday

I only speak positively of others today

7 wednesday

Traditions also provide security

8 thursday

I create the world I live in

friday **9**

Life makes me so happy

  saturday **10**

I enjoy being by myself

 sunday **11**

19:40

I keep discovering new sides to me

wish notes for the week

July 2010 week 28

12 monday

I draw strength from my roots

13 tuesday

I reveal the riches within me

14 wednesday

I dedicate this day to my (inner) children

15 thursday

I put myself first today

friday **16**

I say my wishes out loud

17:10–17:20

saturday **17**

I am special

sunday **18**

Having my own style makes me strong

wish notes for the week

July 2010 week 29

19 monday

My creativity finds the best solutions

20 tuesday

I am a source of inspiration

21 wednesday

I bring more colour into my life

22 thursday

I am full of childish impatience

friday **23**

I can see how multifaceted the world is

saturday **24**

I have so many skills

sunday **25**
'Green Day' according to the
Mayan Calendar

I can also reach my goals playfully

wish notes for the week

July 2010 week 30

26 monday
01:37

I am proud of what I have achieved

27 tuesday

I find the right tone, because it is within me

28 wednesday

I give my day a clear direction

29 thursday

I can make sure I reach my goals

friday **30**

I can express my inner self

 saturday **31**

Friends enrich my life

 sunday **1**

I discover the power within me

wish notes for the week

Successful Ordering

☆☆☆☆

New apartment at the very last moment

Uli lived in a shared apartment and had to move out by a certain date because the apartment was going to be completely renovated and then sold. Uli wasn't worried. He felt absolutely certain that he would find the right place to live and his instinct had never let him down.

It was his landlord, however, who finally began to have doubts. Everybody else had moved out, but Uli was still living in the apartment and the final date for moving was only a week away. It was true that Uli told everyone he met that he needed somewhere new to live, but apart from that he wasn't overstraining himself in actively looking. He felt that there was no need since his instinct still told him that everything would be sorted out in time. The final day, early in the morning, the workmen arrived and began to rip out the old kitchen. Uli still had no idea where he was going to go, so he set off to the corner shop to buy some rolls for breakfast. The shop owner asked him, 'Hey, are you still looking for a new apartment?'

'Yes!'

'Well, we have bought the building diagonally opposite and have to renovate it bit by bit. It'll take a while and if you want you can have one of the apartments for a year. You can move in straight away.'

And that's just what Uli did. He went home, started packing and, piling his belongings onto a wheelbarrow, moved across the street into the building diagonally opposite.

The key to this order is: pay attention to your own instincts and follow them!

Warning: you can only trust this feeling if you are centred and calm and in authentic contact with yourself! Even modern brain research (mirror neuron research – see, for example, *'Why I feel what you feel'* by Joachim Bauer) nowadays confirms that our intuition can switch itself off completely as soon as we are under pressure or stress or allow ourselves to be governed by fear and worry.

There is even a common saying to support this fact – 'Help yourself and God will help you!' – the meaning of which is often slightly misunderstood. It means that godliness can only help you and reach inside you if you ensure that you remain centred and face life calmly and with appreciation. Only then can your intuition function optimally and your feelings show you the way.

Some very simple things are involved in this:

• A healthy diet (e.g. wild herbs, good-quality water etc.)
• Exercise outside in the fresh air, in natural surroundings
• Proximity and connection to other people
• Time for yourself, to relax and to feel inside yourself to see what your heart currently wants you to do, since the universe very seldom calls you by telephone. It contacts you internally through small inner impulses and inspirations. The more experienced you are in feeling inside yourself and becoming aware of your own inner voice, the better you will hear these impulses.

August 2010 week 31

2 monday

I reach my goals

3 tuesday

I write my dreams down

4 wednesday

I dedicate this day to fantasy

5 thursday

Through my dreams I find out about the worlds within r

friday **6**

I am certain of my beliefs

saturday **7**

I live all of my feelings consciously

sunday **8**

My life is valuable

wish notes for the week

August 2010 week 32

9 monday

I use my intuition even at work

10 tuesday
03:08

I trust my inner guide

11 wednesday

I discover my authority

12 thursday

I sense opportunities

friday **13**

I know my inner strength

♎

saturday **14**

I am amazed by daily wonders

sunday **15**

I sense the best decision

wish notes for the week

August 2010 week 33

16 monday

I reveal myself

17 tuesday

17:10–17:20

I can convince through enthusiasm

18 wednesday

Love finds its way in my heart

19 thursday

I open myself to closeness

friday **20**

My feelings lead me to the right place

saturday **21**

I bathe in the rays of love

sunday **22**

The whole truth lies in my feelings

wish notes for the week

August 2010 week 34

23 monday

I share my feelings

24 tuesday
17:05

I am receptive and can express myself well

25 wednesday

I too am allowed to be uncertain

26 thursday

I am learning something new today

week 34 2010 August

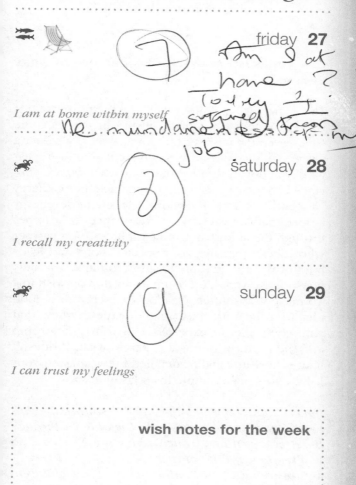

friday **27**

Am I at home?
Today I
suffered from my

I am at home within myself

the mundane ess from my
job

saturday **28**

I recall my creativity

sunday **29**

I can trust my feelings

··
:   :
:   **wish notes for the week**   :
:   :
:   :
··

Successful Wishing

☆☆☆☆

Can you wish yourself the partner of your dreams?

The answer is a definite yes. Using the power of our wishes alone we can make all of our wishes come true – even the wish for our soul partner. Whether a wish is fulfilled or not is solely dependent on what we say about it, think about it or what we are convinced about. This is what affects the etheric energy we send out into the world. This etheric energy is governed by the laws of resonance. It searches through the abundance of possibilities for a partner who exactly matches your specifications and leads both of you to the same location to meet. The only question is, what kind of a partner do you wish for? To make it absolutely clear to yourself, it is a good idea to make a list. Just write down everything that you would like to experience in your relationship and then send it out as a concrete wish. It doesn't matter how unusual or detailed the wishes on your list are – as this example from Jasmine shows:

I was walking through the city. My shift at the university hospital was over and I wandered through the streets as if in a trance asking myself, 'What do you really want out of life?'
My answer was, 'A family, two or three children, a husband, a house with a garden, books and carpets. My husband should both challenge and sup-

port me, his father is a head physician, his mother is from a good family.'

After a while I felt like I wasn't only telling this to myself. Just as the trance was lifting, one more thing came to me: 'He shouldn't still be a student'... and after a pause, 'And a house by the sea would be nice.'

About three weeks later, during my shift at the clinic, I met a doctor... he told me that he had recently passed his final examinations and had just spent three months in the USA as a resident doctor. What can I say? The sparks were flying as we looked at each other and everything else just happened by itself.

He was exactly the man I had imagined as a partner. The funny thing was, his birthday was on the same day as my father's and my father was exactly 35 years older. Everything fitted perfectly. Everything – from the house and the red carpet which we walked down after the wedding ceremony to get to the hotel, from his practice to our holidays – everything came true as I had dreamt it would, down to the smallest detail. Even the house by the sea was there. It belonged to his parents and we went there every year for three weeks in summer with our two sons.

Create a small list with all of your wishes for a wonderful partnership. Find a good place to keep your list safe and then check in one year to see how much of it has already come true. You will be amazed – above all by how powerful your own wish energy can be when you apply it in a targeted way.

Aug/Sept 2010 week 35

30 monday
Summer Bank Holiday

I am full of feeling today

31 tuesday

I take care of my inner child today

1 wednesday

The best solution is when both win

2 thursday

I value honest communication

week 35 2010 September

    friday **3**

I give thanks for the abundance in my life

  saturday **4**

I am in perfect harmony with myself and others

   sunday **5**

I encounter everything with a smile

wish notes for the week

September 2010 week 36

6 monday

I stay in control, even in conflicts

7 tuesday

I get to the bottom of things

8 wednesday ◯
10:30

Other people are a mirror for me

9 thursday

I dedicate this day to a friend

friday **10**

I discover my body today

saturday **11**

I can resolve every argument

sunday **12**

My relationships are my best teacher

wish notes for the week

September 2010 week 37

13 monday

I face up to my fears bravely

14 tuesday

I trust in my creativity

15 wednesday

I surround myself with beauty today

16 thursday

I bring balance to my surroundings

17:10–17:20

friday **17**

I observe the good in others

saturday **18**

I feel loved by everyone today

sunday **19**

I make my dreams come true

wish notes for the week

September 2010 week 38

20 monday

I am generous and charming

21 tuesday

I discover myself in my projections

22 wednesday

I stand by my decisions

23 thursday
Autumn Equinox   09:17

My spiritual growth is important to me

friday **24**

I assert my needs

saturday **25**

My apartment is an expression of my inner satisfaction

sunday **26**

True greatness is shown in resolving an argument

wish notes for the week

Successful Ordering

☆☆☆☆

The self-love mantra

At some point long ago I invented a self-love mantra. It goes like this: 'I love myself and allow myself to be loved.' I told a friend about it, who then recited it in her thoughts repeatedly for a week. She wanted to test out the effect it would have on her marriage. The first to react, though, was her six-year-old daughter. The child liked to hug and cuddle but didn't like kisses. She didn't like being kissed and had never given her mother a kiss and had never once said 'I love you' to her mother.

After the mother had been using the mantra for a week, her daughter came rushing up to her suddenly and cried, 'Mummy, I love you soooo much!' and smothered her mother's arm in kisses – and then her whole face too. This had never happened before. Her mother was flabbergasted by the incredible effectiveness of the mantra.

There was a funny epilogue to this story. I used this as an example in a radio interview to great effect. By chaaaance my friend and her husband were listening to the programme as it went out. 'Hey, that's Barbel, isn't it?' he said in surprise. 'Oh, and that's me she's talking about…' my friend realized and laughed.

And he was impressed, 'Wow, my wife is cited as a

good example on the radio. That's great! And then he put his arms around her and kissed her.

So the mantra did have its effect on him in the end, after a little detour. And my friend recently reported to me that her relationship was going almost suspiciously well at the moment.

Do you know that feeling? 'Too good' and it seems suspicious!? You can heal that too with a little mantra:

• It is my natural state that things are fantastic for me. I allow myself boundless happiness and I willingly share it with others.
• I wish everyone happiness and health their whole life long. (This is a very clever mantra; it includes you and simultaneously prevents any form of guilty conscience about whether it is better to be happier than others.)

You can think of a mantra each morning that will be particularly good at guiding you through the day ahead. Repeat it in your thoughts and feelings whenever you have a moment to spare, so for example at the bus station, on the way to somewhere, while you are tidying up, in the evening in bed, while you are cleaning your teeth in the morning etc.

• I love myself and allow myself to be loved.
• I trust life and look forward eagerly to the wonderful surprises it has in store for me.
• Every crisis brings an opportunity. My self-love shows me the way to grasp this opportunity.
• I love myself, no matter what! I stand by myself.

September 2010 week 39

27 monday

I appreciate the power of my friends

28 tuesday

I draw strength from harmony

29 wednesday

My sensuality is an expression of my lust for life

30 thursday

I give thanks for the beauty that surrounds me

week 39 **2010 October**

friday **1**

I thank my body today

saturday **2**

I am realistic

sunday **3**

I love my life

wish notes for the week

4 monday

I give thanks for my money today

5 tuesday

I give structure to my life today

6 wednesday

I can allocate my powers as I choose

7 thursday
18:44

I am proud of myself

friday **8**

I discover a different point of view

  saturday **9**

I value each person for their individuality

   sunday **10**

I am thankful for my life

wish notes for the week

October 2010 week 41

11 monday

Having responsibility is fun

12 tuesday

I follow my intuition

13 wednesday

I find joy in what I have achieved

14 thursday

I also learn from negative experiences

friday **15**

Harmonious conversations give me joy

saturday **16**

I accept myself the way I am

sunday **17**

17:10–17:20

I thank my family

wish notes for the week

18 monday

3

I carry out my daily tasks with care

19 tuesday

4

I don't have to be perfect in everything I do

20 wednesday

5

I give thanks for all of my relationships today

21 thursday

6

I give myself a present because I am worth it

 friday **22**

It does me good to be kind and caring to others

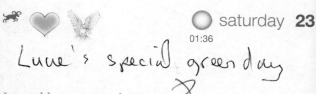 ○ saturday **23**
01:36

Luve's special green day

I am able to accept changes

 sunday **24**

9

I let go of old things

wish notes for the week

October 2010 week 43

25 monday

Every mistake has a deeper meaning for me

26 tuesday

I strive for spiritual clarity

27 wednesday

Even I am allowed to rest

28 thursday

I dress just the way I feel

friday **29**

I can look truth in the eye

saturday **30**

I pay attention to my inner child

sunday **31**
Halloween
End of British Summer time

I have achieved something in life

wish notes for the week

Can You Wish Yourself Healthy Again?

☆☆☆☆

Yes! As the newest scientific findings of epigenetics have proven (this branch of science carries out research into how far we are able to change even our genetic code through the power of our thoughts). It is always the power of human conviction that allows us to become that in which we believe. From health to sickness, from defence by the immune system to the levels of hormones in our bodies, from our power to heal ourselves to our capacity for happiness. As an example to represent many other wonderful stories I will tell you the story of Monika, a young mother, who was able to heal herself by wishing:

Over three years ago, a few days after the birth of our second child I started to have a severe haemorrhage. Apparently there were remnants of the placenta in the womb and the very same day I was given an emergency operation to remove them. The operation was very risky, coming so soon after the birth. I was very worried, and just as I thought I had survived everything, the doctor told me that he had unfortunately not been able to remove everything and that a remnant of the 'placental growth' was still inside me.
From then on I had to go to the hospital each week for a check-up and each time they told me that

unfortunately this remnant would not regress by itself because it was simply too large. A second attempt to scrape it out was planned, but I was very scared of this happening, I didn't want to have a further operation. I had exactly one more week to go.

That very same day I created an affirmation for myself – short and sweet, which I continually turned over in my mind, like a broken record. I said it to myself again and again until it just played along in the background by itself, regardless of what I was saying or doing at the time. Then the day came when the big decision would be taken. Although my rational mind had doubts and in some ways I was preparing myself for the worst (that is to say, the operation) I still went in for the check-up with a strange feeling of inner peace. The doctor didn't say a word to me during the ultrasound. He manoeuvred the device this way and that for ages and then after a while he called another doctor in for a second opinion. My heart was in my mouth because I was sure that something awful had happened.

Then my doctor finally spoke and said that he couldn't understand it and that is why he kept looking again and again; in his opinion it just wasn't possible: he couldn't find ANYTHING. Everything was fine, there was no growth left and so no longer any need for an operation.

I left the hospital dancing with joy! I now know that nothing is impossible if you just believe in it. You carry the reins of your life in your own hands!

There are no boundaries. The only boundaries that exist are in our heads.

November 2010 week 44

1 monday

17

Peace is the path to true power

2 tuesday

18

I explore and discover my surroundings

3 wednesday

19

I am also allowed to be first

4 thursday

Barry's Green Day

20 *I follow my goals with optimism*

friday **5**

21

I use the power of my beliefs

○ saturday **6**
04:52

22

I am constantly improving my life

sunday **7**

23

I am creating my ideal life

wish notes for the week

November 2010 week 45

8 monday

24

I am in contact with my angel

---

9 tuesday

25

I draw strength from my wisdom

---

10 wednesday

26

I accept myself lovingly

---

11 thursday

27

I really do believe in myself today

week 45 2010 November

friday **12**

28

I love and forgive

saturday **13**

1

I make sure that I am balanced

sunday **14**
Remembrance Day

2

I achieve what I am really wishing for

wish notes for the week

November 2010 week 46

15 monday

3

I attach a special meaning to this day

16 tuesday

4

Every day is an ideal day

17 wednesday

5

17:10–17:20

I recognize what is special in each person

18 thursday

6

I live completely from my heart

friday **19**

Each day enriches me and others

saturday **20**

I look forward bravely

 sunday **21**
17:27

I am looking for new meaning

wish notes for the week

November 2010 week 47

22 monday

I bravely step over an inner boundary

23 tuesday

I strive for higher things today

24 wednesday

I look back on my life with satisfaction

25 thursday

I am glad of my independence

friday **26**

I am honest to myself

saturday **27**

I give myself more freedom today

sunday **28**

I bravely step into new areas

wish notes for the week

Nov/Dec 2010 week 48

29 monday

My ideals are becoming clear to me

30 tuesday

I see the goodness in people

1 wednesday

Who am I really?

2 thursday

Forgiveness is the shortest path to personal happiness

week 48 **2010 December**

friday **3**

21

I view the darker sides of me with love

saturday **4**

22

Junk makes me immobile

sunday **5**
17:36

23

I pursue my goals with determination

wish notes for the week

December 2010 week 49

6 monday

24

I let go of something I fear

7 tuesday

25

I accept the lustful side of me

8 wednesday

26

I let go of control

9 thursday

27

I create my own reality

friday **10**

I use the power of thought

saturday **11**

I discover a new side of me

sunday **12**

I examine the restrictions within me today and release them

wish notes for the week

December 2010 week 50

13 monday

The more I am able to let go, the freer I become

14 tuesday

I discover my true nature

15 wednesday

Each person carries their own baggage until they put it down

16 thursday

Old beliefs only have an effect as long as I hold onto them

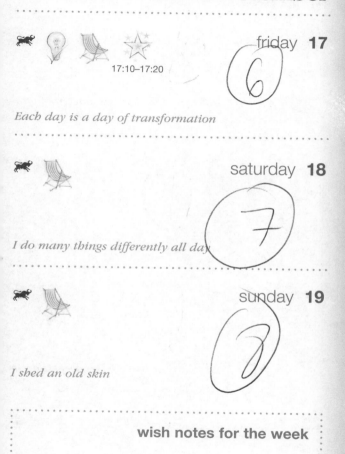

friday **17**

17:10–17:20

6

Each day is a day of transformation

saturday **18**

7

I do many things differently all day

sunday **19**

I shed an old skin

wish notes for the week

December 2010 week 51

20 monday

I relinquish something so as to have room for something new

21 tuesday
Winter Solstice   08:13

I walk my own path alone

22 wednesday

I discover my deepest desire

23 thursday

I stand up for myself with determination

week 51 2010 December

 friday **24**
Christmas Eve

I absorb new influences today

  saturday **25**
Christmas Day

I show myself from my best side

sunday **26**
Boxing Day

I am careful not to control others

wish notes for the week

December 2010 week 52

27 monday

I am creative

28 tuesday

I recognize where I am still fanatical

29 wednesday

I am open to new ideas

30 thursday

I act with emotion and drive

week 52 2010 Dec/Jan 2011

friday **31**
New Year's Eve

I am open to new ideas

saturday **1**
New Year's Day

Each day is a heavenly gift

sunday **2**

This year is a good year

wish notes for the week

My Wish Highlights

☆☆☆☆

Space for notes on wish fulfilment, coincidences or special results.

Personal details:

Name

Address

Telephone no.

Mobile no.

Email

My List of Wishes

☆☆☆☆

① I wish to be Free From the prison of unwanted but deep rooted patterns and programme. The recurring patterns manifest themselves to me so I discover what they are.

② Wish For rupees in India

) Was given a healing session
by Dianne who I met at
the Yoga Village in Kerala.
I am powerful and
I wish to express myself
and be expansive.
Universe - gave me opportunity
to engage in healing and
learn what my limiting
patterns are.
→ Learnt a way to perceive
what my natural tendency
is to become aware of
my inner voice. Was →

skipped a
page by
mistake

My List of Wishes

☆☆☆☆

② Rupees delivered from Luwa's account.

asked to imagine my sofa
at home and how I
perceived to be sitting in it
in my dressage. I was
able to visualise it in my
mind's eye rather than
feel it or hear the noises
→ Tave mere note of
my dreams and visualisations

List of Turbo-wish Dates

☆☆☆☆

_____

_____

_____

_____

_____

_____

_____

_____

_____

_____

_____

_____

_____

_____

The first Red Sea
Diving Resort in
Egypt – possibly
Mohamed Hawash.

Weald + down Forman
lands
Museum